DENTAL DIARIES
THE IRE OF A VAMPIRE

"Hi, I'm Billy Drain. I'm 22 and I'm a vampire. You are about to enter my world… because I'm going to let you read my 'Dental Diaries', my troubled saga. No-no, I don't want your sympathy or any other human feeling that keeps popping up inside you. Just give me your blood. Oh, wait… I have no fangs to extract it. Sigh. Story of my afterlife.

"Anyway, since you're here already, you might as well make yourself useful by reading what I have to say in these pages and write back to me on tinklemail@ack-media telling me how you like my diaries. But before you proceed, there are a few things I'd like to say to you…

"First, whatever you are about to read may be fictitious to you but it has really happened to me.

"Second, whenever you find pages where I have added some extra bytes (that's spelled 'b-y-t-e-s' and not 'b-i-t-e-s'), you will be grateful. It's compulsory.

"Third, you will always be on the lookout for a dentist who is willing (and capable enough) to fix a bloodthirsty vampire's fangs. And when you find such a dentist, you will write to me immediately. Alternately, you can also search for a source of fangs for me.

"Fourth and last, you will always keep your own teeth clean and visit the dentist often… just so I get to look at clean grins when you smile at me in these pages.

"That's all for now. Oh, wait… as is customary, before you start reading someone's book, you get to read all the good things that people have to say about the author. So here you go (don't forget to read my reply to each letter):

This is for Billy Drain: I think you should have false fangs like false teeth.
— **Jeswin Roshan,** *via email*

"Er… the thought did cross my mind, Jeswin. But you see, a vampire's fangs are a complex affair. They need to have channels in them that can inject the victim with venom, as we feed. And I know of no human dentures that do that AND last forever. But if you can find me a pair, I'd be more than happy to try them for a bit."

Billy, you are simply fabulously funny! You are my most favourite toon in the whole of *Tinkle*! I even made a sketch of you, cut it out and stuck it up in my bedroom just underneath a spooky red lamp on the wall.
— **Anisha Jain,** *Uttar Pradesh*

"Why, thank you, Anisha! Red is my favourite colour (can you guess why?). Hehehe."

I wonder when Billy will get his fangs back? I am sure he will look more handsome in them!
— **Kartikeya Reddy,** *via email*

"Oh, you must not make a vampire blush, Kartikeya. It makes them look less ferocious. Heehee."

Billy Drain is more monstrous than us as it is. Imagining how he'll look with fangs gives me the creeps.
— **D. Malavika,** *Chennai*

"You bet. You wouldn't want to meet me in a dark alley then, huh?"

Dental Diaries is superb. In 'Choppy Waters', when Billy says, "D-Does that mean the lagoon is now non-magical and I won't get my fangs this time?", his face is SO cute, I could have jumped into the magazine and hugged him.
— **Clarin Menezes,** *Kuwait*

"Why don't you? Jump into the magazine, I mean. We can have lots of adventures together. I may even take you along on one of my fang-hunting trips."

3

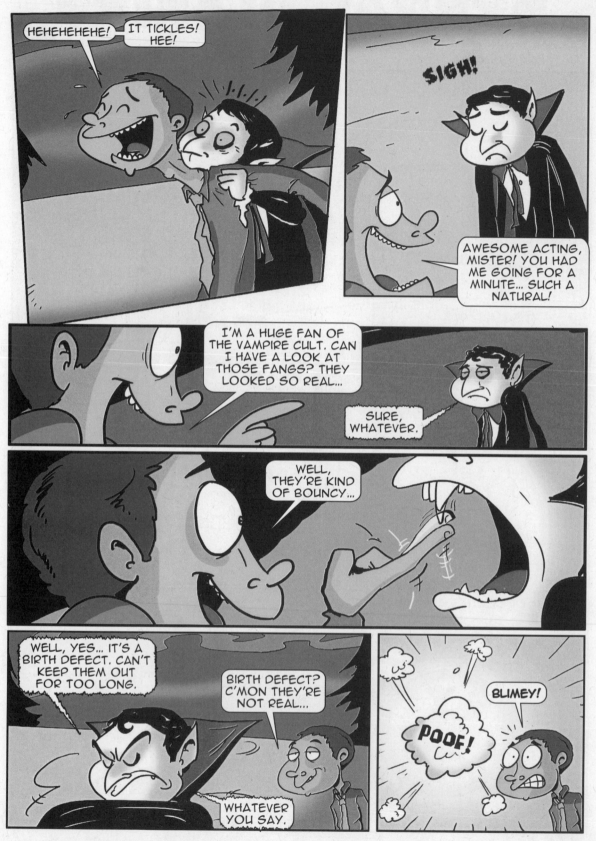

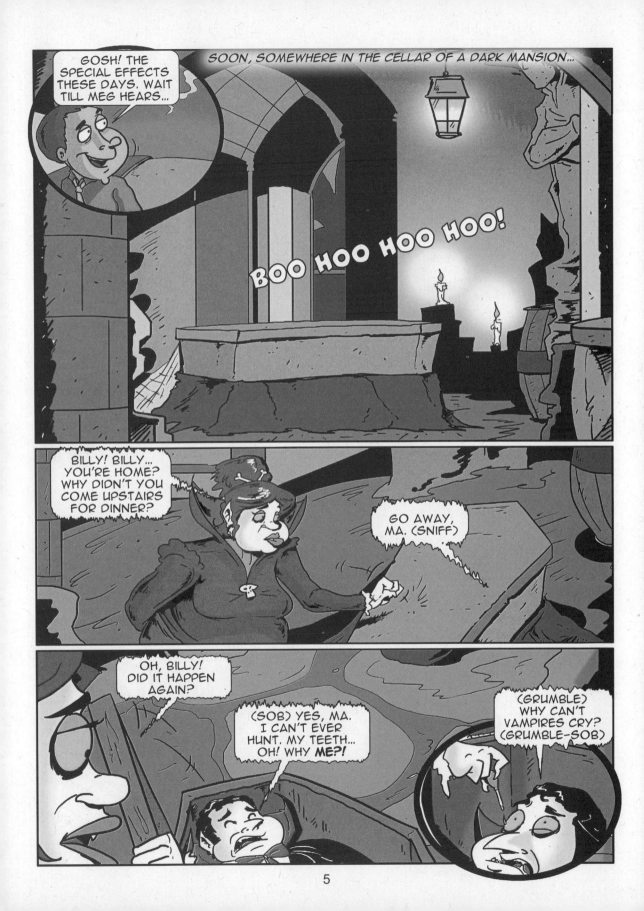

5

6

10

DENTAL DIARIES
FACING THE WORLD

Story & Script
Dolly Pahlajani

Art
Abhijeet Kini

Letters
Pranay Bendre

"THEY'VE TAKEN AWAY EVERYTHING... MY IDENTITY, MY RESPECT... MY FUTURE. LEFT ME USELESS AS A SHADOW DROWNED IN DARKNESS...

"MY CRIME? A PERFECTLY LOGICAL TEMPTATION TO TAKE A BITE OUT OF A DELICIOUS HUMAN DENTIST!

VAMPOLICE

"WHO'D HAVE KNOWN HE WAS PROTECTED BY THE VAMPIRE HIGH COUNCIL*?

"THEY TOOK AWAY MY FANGS! AND I CAN'T EVEN SHED TEARS BECAUSE...

...VAMPIRES CAN'T CRY... (SOB)

*THE COUNCIL THAT GOVERNS VAMPIRES WORLDWIDE

12

IT'S A VAMPIRE'S WORLD!

THAT'S TRUE BECAUSE, YOU SEE, VAMPIRES DON'T EXIST JUST IN THE PAGES OF DENTAL DIARIES. FOLKLORE AROUND THE WORLD IS OVERRIDDEN BY THESE CREATURES OF THE NIGHT (AND SOME THAT EVEN VENTURE OUT DURING DAYTIME). AND I AM HERE TO ENLIGHTEN YOU ABOUT THEM, ON ONE CONDITION—YOU WON'T BE MORE AFRAID OF THEM THAN YOU ARE OF ME. PROMISE?

YARA-MA-YA-WHO AM I?

Yara-ma-yha-who, *Australia*

Although its name sounds like a question, there is no question that this vampire is rather questionable itself. For starters, it is a day hunter. And second and most important, it does not have teeth—nope, not a single. And here I was feeling bad about not having my fangs.

Anyway, since this vampire doesn't have teeth, its fingernails and toenails are equipped with suckers. It generally lives on trees and drops down on unsuspecting travellers to feast on them. And since it is a slow eater, it often stops to rest or nap while feeding.

The aboriginal tribes say that the yara-ma-yha-who looks like a little red man with a very large head… rather like a shell-less watermelon, I think. And despite its large head, it is not big on brains because it can be fooled if its victim plays dead until sunset. After that, it's bedtime for the little guy.

BRAINS ARE REALLY BETTER THAN BRAWN. HE HE HE!

Brahmaparusha, *India*

That's close to home, isn't it? Body as black as soot and hair aglow like lightning, the Brahmaparusha, also known as the Brahmarakshasa, is one of the most fearsome vampires around, and you would do well to steer clear of them. Even though they are from your own country, they are not going to be considerate to you because... you're food. And it's not just your blood the brahmaparusha craves, oh no! It's also your brain (doesn't matter if it's empty). Not to mention the entrails that the brahmaparusha wears as an accessory to show off his hunting skills. If you ask me, this guy's in some serious need of fashion advice. Ugh.

BRAIN TEASERS

AIEE! MARINATED LEGS!

MENU GARLIC + SALT

Wakwak and Manananggal, *Philippines*

Wakwak sounds like the cry of a bird, doesn't it? That's because the creature is a bird… well, that's what Filipino mythology says anyway. The wakwak is said to have bat-like wings and long, sharp talons that it uses to hunt its prey. Any guesses what the prey may be? Hehehe.

And if a flying bird-vampire isn't enough, there is always the Manananggal who is just as complicated as its name. The Manananggal is a vampire who is capable of dividing its body into two. Its torso is said to sprout wings and take flight when it hunts at night. But while it leaves its extra baggage (lower body) behind, someone can come and sprinkle salt or apply crushed garlic to it. This is said to stop the torso from being able to rejoin the rest of the body, effectively finishing off the Manananggal. Now if I were a Manananggal, I would simply pack my 'better half' in a bag and take it with me. Heehee.

Varcolaci, *Romania*

One of the most ancient and most powerful vampire species ever, the Varcolaci are known for their appetite. Not just for human prey, but for the sun and the moon. You heard that right! When the Varcolaci feel like eclipsing the moon or the sun, they simply fall into a deep, deep sleep (zzzzzz!) and their spirit then flies out to do some celestial chomping. It is said that if their bodies are moved while their spirits are away, then they can never make it back to their forms.

Mostly, the Varcolaci are shown in pairs and they are believed to take various forms such as small dogs or dragons. In their human forms, Varcolaci are known by their pale faces and dry skin. I wonder if they've heard of moisturizers...

MINE!

NO WAY! IT'S MY DINNER!

MY PREY IS A HOP, SKIP AND JUMP AWAY!

Jiangshi, *China*

This one jumps a lot, like it's on a pogo stick. Dressed in traditional clothes of the Qing Dynasty (the last imperial dynasty of China), hands outstretched and a spring in its step (literally!), the Jiangshi is known as the 'hopping vampire'. The term 'jiang' in Chinese means 'hard' or 'stiff' and the Jiangshi is said to have such stiff limbs and joints that it has no choice but to hop around if it has to get somewhere. Whoever heard of an arthritic vampire?!

The Jiangshi is said to kill living things and absorb their life force, known as 'qi', hoping that when it has enough, it may return to life. But before it does, it needs a bath with some serious scrubbing. Why? Well, the Jiangshi is said to have greenish skin (could be fungus or mould growing on the corpse) and white hair. *Ugh. I need a wash now.*

COUNT ALL THESE? BUT I CAN COUNT ONLY TILL 10!

Soucouyant or Loogaroo, *Caribbean*

An old woman by day, a fireball by night—this vampire certainly has a happening afterlife. Once the sun sets, the old woman sheds her skin, hides it in mortar (I wonder if that gives her a sense of 'stability'?) and turns into a fireball that flies into the homes of unsuspecting, sleeping people. The fireball needs no more than a crack or a keyhole to enter the human home and feast on its victims.

To stop a soucouyant, it is said that one must spill rice in its path. Seeing the scattered grains, the soucouyant has no option but to sit down and count each one. That's some serious obsession with rice.

Rice reminds me... I'm rather hungry. *Prey for me?*

Text: Dolly Pahlajani   Illustrations: Abhijeet Kini   Layout: Jitendra Patil

DENTAL DIARIES
MUMMY KNOWS BEST (Part 2)

Story & Script	**Art**	**Letters**
Dolly Pahlajani	Abhijeet Kini	Pranay Bendre

"VAMPIRES. WE'RE MAJESTIC CREATURES OF THE NIGHT. BUT WHAT HAPPENS WHEN OUR FANGS ARE TAKEN AWAY? WE'RE REDUCED TO ROBBING DENTURES FROM DUSTY, OLD MEN WRAPPED IN BANDAGES.

THE SEARCH FOR PHARAOH SEKHMET SABRE'S MAGIC GOLD DENTURES BROUGHT MUMMY AND ME (I'M BILLY DRAIN, BY THE WAY) TO THE LAND OF THE PYRAMIDS. BUT THINGS WEREN'T GOING SO WELL. AND MY GLEAMING NEW FANGS WERE OF LITTLE USE AGAINST AN ANGRY MUMMY."

NO. ONE. TAKES. MY. THINGS. GIVE. THOSE. TEETH. BACK.

HE'S STRONG ENOUGH TO SNAP MY NECK. AND THEN... I'LL NEED A PERMANENT GRAVE. BETTER GET MOM AND LEAVE.

POOF!

THAT'S MY HEART, YOU THIEVING WOMAN!

POOF!

WHAT DO YOU NEED IT FOR? GO BACK TO SLEEP!

MUMMY!

WHAT?!

?!

28

SUCKER PUNS

- Dolly Pahlajani
Art and Design: Ira Anand

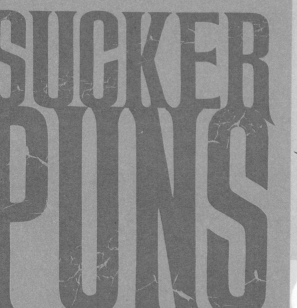

Who says that we vampires don't have a sense of humour? Here's a set of my favourite vampire puns that will 'suck' the laughter right out of you!

Why did the vampire keep turning up his nose at people?
He was very vein.

Why did the vampire hate her job?
Because it was draining

What do you do when you hit a vampire with footwear?
Shoebite!

I am all keyed up!

What does a computer-savvy vampire do?

He bytes.

A doctor a day keeps pressures away!

Why did the vampire go to the physician?

To check her blood pressure.

I never leave my fans high and dry. Ha!

How do you know that a vampire is famous?

When she has a fang club.

33

GOBBLE!

BURRRP!

HUH? DID I JUST GET EATEN BY A MIRROR?

BILLY BABY! YOU TOO?

MOMMY! WHY ARE YOU LOOKING SO PALE? I CAN ALMOST SEE THROUGH YOU!

IT'S THIS MIRROR. IT'S HOLDING US HERE, FEEDING ON US TILL WE BECOME REFLECTIONS OF OURSELVES.

IS THERE NO WAY OUT?

THUMP

NO, I'VE TRIED. BUT, IT'S NOT LETTING ME LOOK OUT, LET ALONE GET OUT.

BUT, YOU JUST CALLED OUT TO ME AND I SAW YOU LOOKING OUT...

IT MUST HAVE BEEN THE MIRROR'S WAY OF LURING YOU IN. IT'S SMART, THIS MIRROR. WE'RE DONE FOR.

The Fang Anthem

– By Billy Drain

Two pointy canines
Two pointy canines
Two pointy canines of mine
Oh, one day I'm going to find
Soon I'm going to find
Two pointy canines and make them mine!

Hide them anywhere
Hide them anywhere
Hide them anywhere in the world
Oh-ho, those shiny suckers
Those pointy suckers
Hide them anywhere, it's futile!

And when I have my fangs
And when I have my fangs
And when I have my fangs in my mouth
You humans will toe the line
I'll make you toe the line
You'll have to toe the line all the time!

I'll top the food chain
I'll top the food chain
I'll top the food chain once again
Oh-ho, that will be divine
It will be so divine
Yum-slurp-chomp-gulp-yummy, so divine!

Oh, you won't feel a thing
Oh, you won't feel a thing
Oh, you won't feel a thing, sweet prey of mine
Oh-ho, simply close your eyes,
Sweet-smelling prey of mine
Oh, nervous prey of mine, it's just one bite!

JOIN ME AS I PLEDGE THAT I WILL NOT REST IN PEACE UNTIL I FIND MY FANGS. SING THIS ANTHEM WITH ME. SING TO THE TUNE OF 'WE SHALL OVERCOME (HUM HONGE KAAMYAAB)'.

Text: Dolly Pahlajani   Layout: Jitendra & Pranay   Illustration: Abhijeet Kini

DENTAL DIARIES

Story & Script Dolly Pahlajani **Art** Abhijeet Kini **Letters** Pranay Bendre

CHOPPY WATERS

"THAT FACE HAUNTS MY NIGHTMARES...

...OR MAYBE THEY'RE 'DAY'MARES, BECAUSE WE VAMPIRES SLEEP DURING THE DAY. WHATEVER THEY ARE, THEY KEEP REPLAYING ONE TRACK...

"...MY END... AT THE HANDS OF MYRA VAMPTOP MY BEAUTIFUL, BLOODTHIRSTY NEIGHBOUR* AND HER...

...CAAAAAAT!

SNIGGER-MEOW-SNIGGER

WHO'S THAT?

MEOW!

SSSPIT!

THUMP

WHY YOU LITTLE FELINE FREAK! GO BACK TO YOUR MISTRESS!

BILLY BABY, THAT'S THE THIRD TIME YOU'VE THROWN POOR MR. CHUCKLES OUT OF BED BECAUSE OF YOUR NIGHTMARES.

B-BUT, MOM, THE CAT... IT...

39

*"Remember the dentist I'd attacked? Well, that was Myra's uncle. So, I'm her sworn enemy, much against my wish."

*"It's true. Never will you meet a vampire who'll willingly cross water. So, to keep us going, Mom has had our diving suits specially lined with the earth that fills our coffins. Thank heavens we don't need to breathe. I don't know how humans bear it."

**"It's a ring-shaped coral reef which surrounds a lagoon. Thank me later for that tidbit. I'm diving into the deep now."

42

*"Even through my pain, let me tell you that lunar eclipses are far from short. But this one was mercifully brief."

44

46

DENTAL DIARIES
TINGLE ALL THE WAY

Concept & Art
Abhijeet Kini

Story & Script
Dolly Pahlajani

Letters
Prasad & Pranay

DAWN IS CLOSE. SOON, HERE WILL LIE A CRISPY, SUN-DRIED VERSION OF ME. COMPLIMENTS OF THE CHEF, MYRA VAMPTOP.

"THE PLAN MYRA 'COOKED UP' TRICKED MOMMY AND ME INTO COMING TO THIS ATOLL IN FIJI TO LOOK FOR FANGS. INSTEAD, WE FOUND BLOODTHIRSTY WEREMAIDS. AND THOUGH WE SURVIVED THEM, WE CAN'T SURVIVE THE SUN WHICH WILL BE UP IN A FEW HOURS.

"WE'RE MAROONED, SURROUNDED BY FLOWING WATER AND THE ONLY SURVIVAL PLAN IS TO...

...MAKE A WISH. YEAH. RIGHT.

WE'RE GRASPING AT STRAWS. BUT THEY'RE AS INFLAMMABLE AS US.

BILLY DEAR, DO STOP YOUR MUTTERING AND LET ME MAKE MY WISH BEFORE THE SUN COMES UP...

UMMM... OKAY, MOMMY. BUT ARE YOU SURE YOU'RE NOT WISHING FOR AN EARLY SUNRISE?

WHAT! WHERE?

THERE! IT'S THE SUN! WE'RE GOING TO DIEEEEE!

48

MEANWHILE, IN THE DRAIN MANSION...

PHUMP

PHOO!

THERE-THERE, YOUNG MAN. LET ME HELP YOU UP.

YOU KEEP AWAY FROM HIM.

B-BUT, MOMMY. HE JUST SAVED US, DIDN'T HE?

NO, HE DIDN'T. HE MADE A DEAL, REMEMBER? AND NOW WE HAVE TO PAY HIM.

THE AGREEMENT IS RIGHT HERE, MADAME. TIME TO HONOUR IT, PLEASE...

AGREEMENT

...BEFORE MY BRAINDEER GET HUNGRY. AND DEMAND VAMPIRES FOR SUPPER.

WOAH. WHATEVER HAPPENED TO KINDNESS AND FREE GIFTS?

WHAT DO YOU TAKE ME FOR? SANTA CLAUS? YOU NEED TO BE ALIVE TO AVAIL HIS SERVICES.

HERE YOU GO.

WHY, THANK YOU, MA'AM.

WHAT'S IN IT?

49

53

*"Just so you know—night-rogen gas is a liquid at very low temperatures. Any contact with liquid night-rogen causes rapid freezing. No wonder poor Zombie Claws turned into a zomb-cicle!"

** "Did you know the nasal passage leads straight to the brain? In fact, in Ancient Egypt, during mummification, the brain of the dead person was pulled out through the nose. Awesomely gross, huh?"

DENTAL DIARIES

Story & Script Dolly Pahlajani   **Art** Abhijeet Kini   **Letters** Pranay Bendre

*TRANSLATION: DESTRUCT.

*Legends say that ghouls usually ate people who passed through places haunted by them, unless those people paid them. And the wise ones usually did. After all, watching your hard-earned money being taken away is far less painful than journeying through the smelly digestive tract of a ghoul!

*"For those who're ignorant, the Tooth Fairy's wand does not affect animals. So, Grisanta was my trump card and my backup as I handed that wand to HelSingh to test his loyalty. Oh, what would I do without her!"

THE LIVING BEHIND THE UNDEAD

HEY! DENTAL DIARIES IS MY LIFE SAGA. I WRITE AND DRAW IT SINGLE-HANDEDLY. I DON'T KNOW WHY THESE TWO HUMANS ARE TAKING ALL THE CREDIT. I–I'LL BITE... UH, SUE THEM! I WILL!

Dolly Pahlajani, *Writer*

Teehee! I bet Billy has told you that he writes and draws the entire series himself. Well, we let him keep thinking that... just so he does not dwell too much on his lost fangs. We don't want him to get all depressed, do we?

So, where were we? Ah, writing Dental Diaries. Well, it's pure joy! Billy breaks all the rules... he likes talking to humans. You'll often find him chatting with you, dear reader, bang in the middle of a comic. He likes to think he's a threat to humankind... but we all (including me) find him extremely adorable, like a cuddly toy. And he makes a great travelling companion too. Confused?

Well, the thing is that I live quite far away from the *Tinkle* office. And it's a solid two-hour commute getting to work every day. So, I often use that time to think of stories and plots. You'd find me scribbling away in my notebook, lost in the middle of a local train's peak hour crowd. On one such day, when I was feeling particularly wonky, Billy was born. And so taken was I by the idea of a vampire losing his fangs because of a dentist, that I kept muttering story dialogues (and spooking passersby by bursting into sudden solitary giggles) all the way until I got to my desk, and even after that! And then I bit my nails as Rajani, the editor, read the script. I was immensely surprised and pleased that she liked it (she doesn't prefer horror, as a rule) and let me run it.

Of course, the next step was the art. And I could think of no one but Abhijeet for the illustrations. His loopy art style and our shared love for the supernatural seemed just perfect for my little, loony, fangless vampire. And when he sent in the sketches for Billy... it was exactly how I'd imagined him! A scrawny 22-year-old vampire who has never hunted in his life... and consequently, looks malnourished and has a stunted growth, making him scared of the big, bad world. But, you, dear readers, make the world a happy place for Billy. Thank you for accepting him as your friend.

Abhijeet Kini, *Artist*

I absolutely love Billy Drain. He's the real new-age vampire, if you ask me. He faces real-world problems (including major dental issues), gets pampered like crazy by his mom, gets to travel around the world and still manages to get into enough trouble to get another episode of mayhem out. Dental Diaries is an extremely different kind of series, quite unconventional, yet with a universal appeal. Sure, it has its gore, scary moments and monsters, but that's the healthy amount of it. Not too much, not too little.

I remember when Dolly called me up and told me that there was a script she had written which I would find pretty interesting, I knew something was up. There was evil laughter in her voice. And then it was in my inbox in just a few minutes. I opened the document and I was soon laughing out loud. A young vampire, with a massive confidence issue and to top it all... a missing pair of fangs! It couldn't get any better than this. I went all out with it, adding as much blacks as I could, since Dental Diaries is a 'black comedy'. Till date, after so many episodes, Dental Diaries is a series that keeps me on my toes; I can never be too sure what's coming next—a mummy here, a ghoul there, a werewolf here and there. I can go crazy with the art for this series, as Dolly makes sure she gives me a vast playground to hit the ball out of the park, with ghouls and demons I have grown up watching in movies or reading in folklore. If you are into a little madness mixed with friendly horror, Dental Diaries is the perfect read for you!

Layout: Jitendra Patil

THE MONSTROUS QUIZ

IF YOU'VE BEEN PAYING ATTENTION TO MY DIARY, YOU WILL BE ABLE TO SOLVE THIS PUZZLE HANDS DOWN. READY?

1. I came across a monster with a past tense verb in its name. □□□□□□□○

2. This undead hunter's wand looks like a giant ○□□□□□□□□○□.

3. The first name of my mother: □□□□□□.

4. My father is professionally a □□□□□□□○.

5. The name of my favourite fangless teddy bear is Mr. □□□□□□□□.

6. On the night of a hunter's moon, the colour of the moon is □○□.

7. The feline vampire who spies on me all the time: □□○□□□□□

8. His first name is the object I covet so much: □□□□ □□□□□□□□

9. They prance through the night sky drawing a sleigh: □□□□□○□□□

10. Never ever make a wish to this guy unless you absolutely have no other choice: □□□□□□ □□□□○

Now the circled letters form a jumbled word. Unscramble it to find the name of a species I am most afraid of. ○○○○○○○○

Text: Dolly Pahlajani   Layout: Jitendra Patil